You're hired

by Jayne Garner

Acknowledgements

Actor: David Shuker

Copyright © Axis Education 2011

First published in Great Britain by Axis Education Ltd

ISBN 978-1-84618-214-3

Axis Education
PO Box 459
Shrewsbury
SY4 4WZ

Email: enquiries@axiseducation.co.uk

www.axiseducation.co.uk

Here's a job for a farm hand. Could I work on a farm?

I could, but I prefer to work in town. There's always plenty to do in town. It would be too quiet on a farm. No, that's not the job for me.

Here's a job driving a truck. Could I work as a lorry driver?

I can drive a car but to drive a lorry you need an HGV licence. I'm not sure I'd like to drive all day. I prefer working in a team. No, that's not the job for me.

Here's a job working in IT. Could I work in IT?

I could, but every time I touch a computer
something goes wrong. I don't like computers and
they don't like me. No, that's not the job for me.

Here's a job for a painter. Could I work as a painter?

I could, but I think painting is too boring. I can't see me standing with a brush and roller all day long. I prefer to do something with a bit more variety. No, that's not the job for me.

Here's a job working on an oil rig. Could I work on an oil rig?

I could, but I don't want to have to go away to work. I prefer to work in my home town. You have to go away for weeks at a time on an oil rig. No, that's not the job for me.

Here's a job working at the airport. Could I work at the airport?

I could, but the airport is out of town. I prefer to work right in the town centre. The trip all the way out to the airport each day would take too long. No, that's not the job for me.

Here's a job working at the circus. Could I work as a circus clown?

I could, but there is no way I would wear that silly
outfit. I like to wear my own clothes to work.
Wearing a clown suit would be too embarrassing.
No, that's not the job for me.

Here's a job working at the hospital. Could I work at the hospital?

I could, but I really can't stand the smell of hospitals. The smell of disinfectant makes me feel ill. No, that's not the job for me.

I've looked at lots of jobs in the paper but none of them are quite right. What job can I do?

Den thinks long and hard. What do I want from a job? What do I like?

I want to work in town and I want to work in a team. I like to work with my friends and I like to lay tiles.

I already have a job that is perfect for me. I think I'd better stick with that!